NATURE
CYCLES

FIRST
GRAPHICS

WATER
GOES ROUND
THE WATER CYCLE

BY
ROBIN KOONTZ

ILLUSTRATED BY
CHRIS DAVIDSON

Raintree

www.raintreepublishers.co.uk
Visit our website to find out
more information about
Raintree books.

To order:
☎ Phone 0845 6044371
🖶 Fax +44 (0) 1865 312263
✉ Email myorders@raintreepublishers.co.uk

Customers from outside the UK please telephone +44 1865 312262

Raintree is an imprint of Capstone
Global Library Limited,
a company incorporated in England
and Wales having its
registered office at 7 Pilgrim Street,
London, EC4V 6LB
– Registered company number:
6695582

Designed by Lori Bye and
   Victoria Allen
Art Director Nathan Gassman
Production by Victoria Fitzgerald
Originated by Capstone Global
   Library Ltd.
Printed and bound in China by
   Leo Paper Products Ltd.

ISBN 978 1 406 23007 9
15 14 13 12 11
10 9 8 7 6 5 4 3 2 1

**British Library Cataloguing in
   Publication Data**
Koontz, Robin Michal.
   Water goes round : the water
cycle. -- (Nature cycles)
   1. Hydrologic cycle--Comic books,
strips, etc.--Juvenile
   literature.
   551.4'8-dc22

Disclaimer
All the Internet addresses (URLs)
given in this book were valid at the
time of going to press. However,
due to the dynamic nature of the
Internet, some addresses may have
changed, or sites may have changed
or ceased to exist since publication.
While the author and Publishers
regret any inconvenience this may
cause readers, no responsibility for
any such changes can be accepted
by either the author or
the Publishers.

Contents

Water, water everywhere

Water covers most of the Earth.

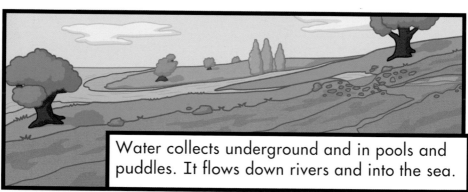

Water collects underground and in pools and puddles. It flows down rivers and into the sea.

Water is also frozen in snow and ice.

Even the clouds are made of water.

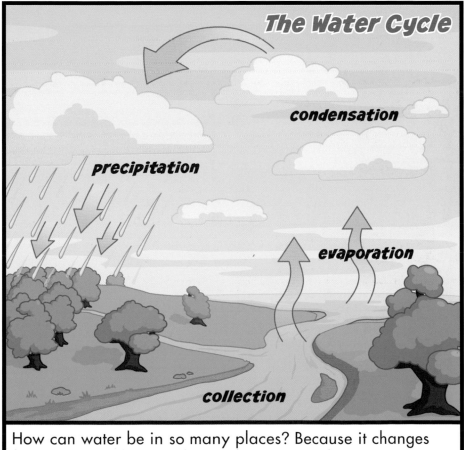

The Water Cycle

condensation

precipitation

evaporation

collection

How can water be in so many places? Because it changes form again and again during the water cycle.

Disappearing act!

Have you ever seen a puddle shrink on a sunny day? Where does the water go?

Evaporation makes the water disappear.

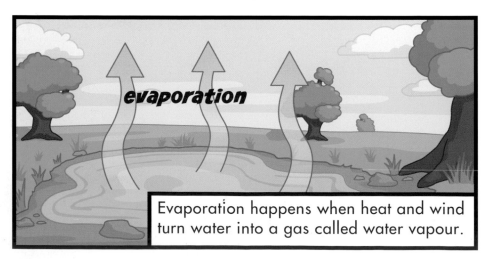

evaporation

Evaporation happens when heat and wind turn water into a gas called water vapour.

Water vapour forms over lakes, rivers, sea, and land.

lake

river

sea

Wind carries water vapour into the air.
The water vapour cools as it rises.

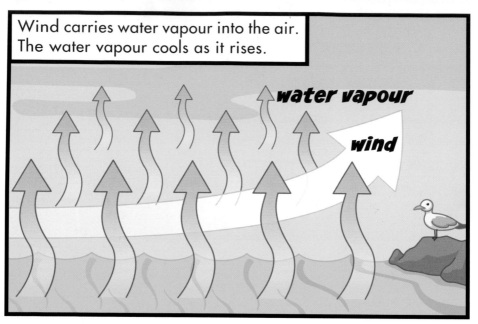

water vapour

wind

This cooling causes condensation.
Condensation changes water vapour back to
a liquid. Tiny water droplets form in the air.

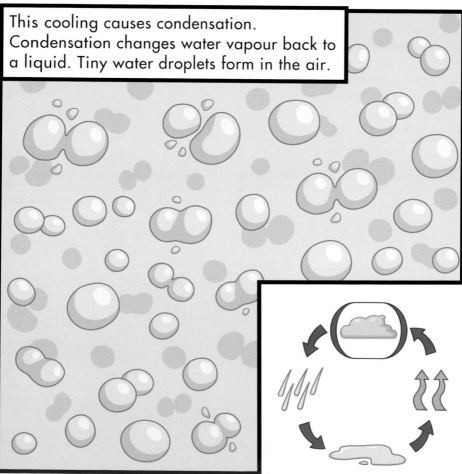

These droplets stick to tiny bits of dust, salt, or smoke.

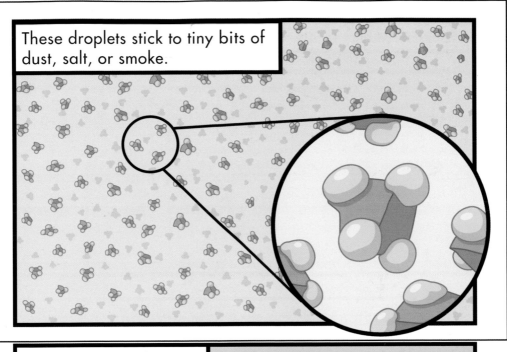

Many dusty droplets join together to form clouds.

stratus clouds

cumulus clouds

cirrus clouds

Clouds carry water around the Earth.

Along the way, the clouds change shape. Water droplets inside clouds continue to evaporate and condense.

The clouds grow larger and darker as more water vapour condenses.

Over time, clouds grow heavy with water. The sky grows dark.

What goes up must come down

Water droplets bounce into each other inside clouds.

They stick together to form larger droplets.

The droplets grow too heavy for the cloud. They fall as precipitation.

Precipitation is an important step in the water cycle. It brings water back to Earth.

Rain is the most common form of precipitation.

Rain is only one form of precipitation. Water droplets freeze at 0 degrees Celsius (32 degrees Fahrenheit). They fall as snow, sleet, or hail.

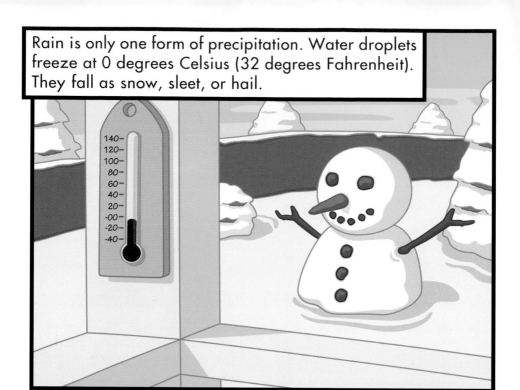

Snowflakes form when water droplets freeze and stick together in the clouds.

Sometimes snow is light and fluffy.

Sometimes it is wet and sticky.

Snowball fight!

Sleet is tiny ice pellets. It forms when snowflakes thaw and refreeze as they fall.

Hail forms in strong thunderstorms. These balls of ice can grow larger than golfballs.

A gathering of drops

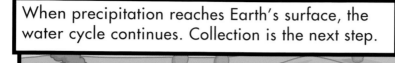

When precipitation reaches Earth's surface, the water cycle continues. Collection is the next step.

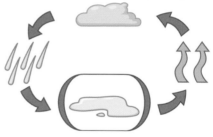

Most precipitation soaks into the ground. It gathers as surface water and groundwater.

Some water stays close to Earth's surface. It soaks into the soil and provides water for plants and trees.

Surface water moves through the soil. It seeps into streams.

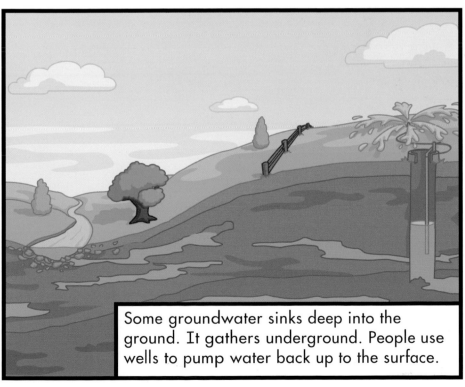

Some groundwater sinks deep into the ground. It gathers underground. People use wells to pump water back up to the surface.

Precipitation also gathers above ground. Snow and ice melt to become liquid.

Water collects in puddles and runs into streams.

It flows downhill into rivers, tumbles over waterfalls, and spills into lakes.

In time, some of the water travels back to the sea.

An endless water cycle

All water makes up the water cycle. The water cycle goes round and round.

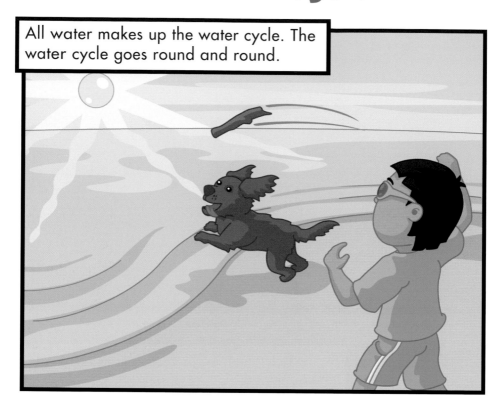

Water evaporates into water vapour. It rises into the sky and condenses into clouds.

Water droplets in the clouds grow heavy.

The drops fall as precipitation. The water collects in groundwater, streams, and rivers.

Then water flows all the way back to the sea. The water cycle never ends.

Glossary

collection   the act of gathering something

condensation   the act of turning from a gas into a liquid

cycle   something that happens over and over again

droplet   very small drop of liquid

evaporation   the act of turning from a liquid to a gas

gas substance that spreads to fill any space that holds it

groundwater   water that is found underground

precipitation   all forms of water that fall from clouds. Forms of precipitation include rain, snow, and hail.

vapour   gas made from a liquid

Find out more

Books

Earth's Water Cycle (Planet Earth), Amy Bauman (Gareth Stevens, 2008)

How the Water Cycle Works (Our Earth), Jen Green (PowerKids Press, 2008)

Project X: The Water Cycle, Steve Parker (Oxford University Press, 2009)

The Water Cycle (Nature's Cycles), Sally Morgan (Wayland, 2009)

Websites

http://www.kidzone.ws/water/
Visit this website for some more fun facts about the water cycle and how it works.

http://www.epa.gov/safewater/kids/flash/flash_watercycle.html
Watch a cartoon about the water cycle.

http://www.actewagl.com.au/education/_lib/Flash/Water_cycle/water.swf
Learn more about the water cycle and how we use water on this interactive website.

Index